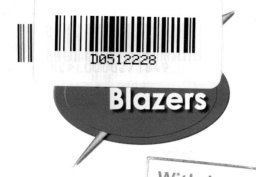

Blazers

Weird Creatures

by David Orme

Rans⊕m

Trailblazers

Weird Creatures
by David Orme
Educational consultant: Helen Bird

Illustrated by Stefan Lindblad

Published by Ransom Publishing Ltd.
51 Southgate Street, Winchester, Hants. SO23 9EH
www.ransom.co.uk

ISBN   978 184167 799 6
First published in 2009

Illustrations copyright © 2009 Stefan Lindblad
'Get the Facts' section - images copyright: leaf insect, stick insect - Eric Isselée; aye-aye - Andrew Ciscel; white-faced saki - Skyscraper; 'little Dumbo' octopus - NASA; leafy sea dragon - Wendy Rathey; ocellated frogfish - Nick Hobgood; Cappadocia, Turkey - Vladimir Melnik; diver and fish - Jodi Jacobson; river crayfish - Leonid Nyshko; cave crayfish - Andy King/U.S. Fish and Wildlife Service; Texas blind salamander - Joe N. Fries/U.S. Fish and Wildlife Service; Judean desert - David Shankbone; Thorny devil - Bäras; Kangaroo rat - U.S. Fishand Wildlife Service; Prairie dog - Joanna Pecha; Emperor penguins - Jan Will, Alexander Hafemann; technician - Kenn Wislande; Grand Prismatic Spring, Yellowstone National Park - Chris Williams

Every effort has been made to locate all copyright holders of material used in this book. If any errors or omissions have occurred, corrections will be made in future editions of this book.

A CIP catalogue record of this book is available from the British Library.

Weird Creatures

Contents

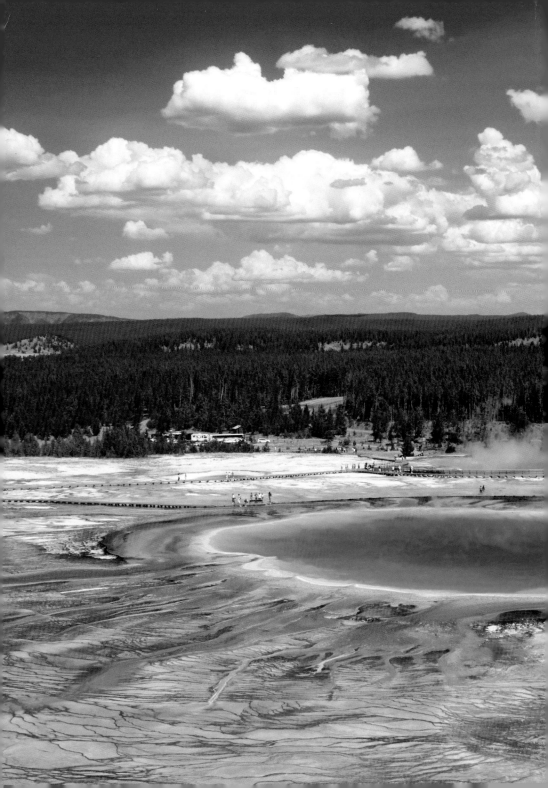

Weird Creatures

Get the facts

Weird quiz

Q Which of these are **real** animals, and which ones are **fake** pictures?

1

2

3

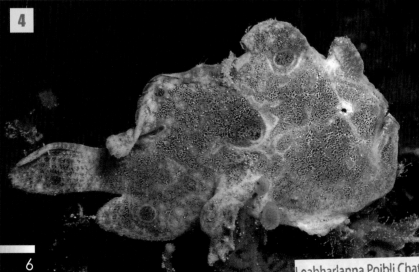

4

5

7

6

8

9

A **They are all real!**
These are just some of
the weird creatures that
live on **Planet Earth!**

*The creatures are
listed on page 36.*

A weird environment – the deep ocean

200 metres down, it's very cold and very dark. At 1,000 metres, there is **no light** left at all. This deep, the **water pressure** is huge – humans can only survive in **submarines** made of thick steel.

Some of the **world's** **weirdest creatures** live here.

This kind of squid is **transparent** – so other fish can't see it!

Some fish can light up parts of their bodies. They do this to **attract a mate** – or tempt the next meal to come close!

Small fish love the **bright lights** – but coming close is a **BIG mistake!**

This **jellyfish** lives at the bottom of the deep sea.

Cave creatures

Many creatures spend part of their lives in caves.

Some never come out. These animals are called **troglobites**.

A **dark, wet cave** sounds like a bad place to live. *So why do some creatures live there?*

- There aren't many **predators**.
- The **temperature** stays the same all the year round.

But what is there to eat?

The water that flows into caves brings food.

An important food for cave insects is **bat droppings**. Bats like to sleep and hibernate in caves.

These are both **crayfish**. One lives in a cave, and one doesn't.

Which is which?

The one on the right lives in the cave. It has **no eyes**, and has lost its colour.

WHY?

Eyes and **colour** aren't much use in a cave! The fish living in caves have **adapted** to the place they are living in. This may have taken many thousands of years.

This is a **Texas blind salamander**. It spends its whole life in pitch dark caves.

How does it find its food without eyes?

Like the crayfish, it has developed a good sense of smell to find the tiny creatures that it eats.

What weird creatures live in these caves?

Humans! (*Well, they used to.*)

Desert creatures

During the day, the **temperature** in deserts can be over **50 degrees centigrade**.

There may be little or no water.

How can animals survive here?

● Most desert animals shelter in **burrows** in the day. They only look for food in the evening and night, when it is cooler. Their bodies are **adapted** so they lose as little water as possible.

Kangaroo rat

These critters live in the **driest deserts** and are one of the **most amazing** animals on Earth.

They can live without any water at all – yet their bodies have the same amount of water as other animals!

How come?

They are able to change completely dry food like seeds into water inside their bodies.

They can take in any water from the air by breathing it in through their noses. Oh, and they don't **sweat** or **urinate**.

Prairie dog

It doesn't look much like a dog to me.

That's because it is really a type of **squirrel**. It lives in huge 'cities' in American deserts. About **400 million** prairie dogs live in the biggest city, which is in **Texas**.

Thorny devil

This creature from **Australia** looks scary, but it is really quite timid.

What the thorny devil really loves is **ants**. One meal can be as many as **3,000 ants** – all eaten one at a time!

In an hour it can polish off at least 1,000 ants!

13

Out in the cold

Now here's a really weird creature.

No it's not – it's a penguin!

Emperor penguins like this are one of the Earth's **most amazing** creatures.

They live happily in **Antarctica**, the coldest place on Earth. In winter, temperatures can be as low as **minus 90 degrees centigrade!**

Penguins can't fly. Is that right?

Wrong! They can. They fly – **under water!**

Their **short flippers** are perfect for this special sort of flight.

14

The world's most boring job

The female emperor penguin lays an **egg**, then hands it over to **Dad**. He **keeps it warm** in a **special pouch**.

So why is that boring?

The **female penguin** has headed out to sea, to have a **good feed**. He has to stand there, in the freezing cold, for around **sixty days**, waiting for the egg to hatch. He can't feed, or do anything much at all.

Anybody want to play 'I Spy'?

I wonder what he thinks about.

Can he move about?

He can **shuffle** a bit – but you try walking with an egg balanced on your feet!

15

Extremophiles

Here are some of the most **extreme environments** on Earth.

- **Hot springs** where the temperature is hotter than boiling water.

- Inside **hot desert rocks**.

- Places where there is **deadly radiation**.

Living things can be found in all of these places.

Hot spring, Yellowstone ...

This is a **black smoker**. It is a **volcano** deep in the **ocean**.

Down here, there is no light and very little oxygen. The temperatures can be as high as 110 degrees centigrade.

Amazingly, there are **many creatures** that live here. The **heat** and **chemicals** from the volcano provide the **energy** that they need.

The world's ultimate survivor –
The Water Bear

These tiny guys can live –
anywhere! They have been
found:

- on the top of Everest
- under layers of ice
- in hot springs
- in places where there is dangerous radiation.

They can survive being heated to 200 degrees
centigrade, and frozen at minus 200 degrees!

Creatures like these are
called **extremophiles**.

Scientists find them really
interesting.

They can survive in the
vacuum you find in **space**.

If the going gets tough,
they can dry themselves
out completely and survive
for up to ten years.

If creatures can live in all
these places on Earth,
maybe life can exist in
extreme conditions on
other planets.

17

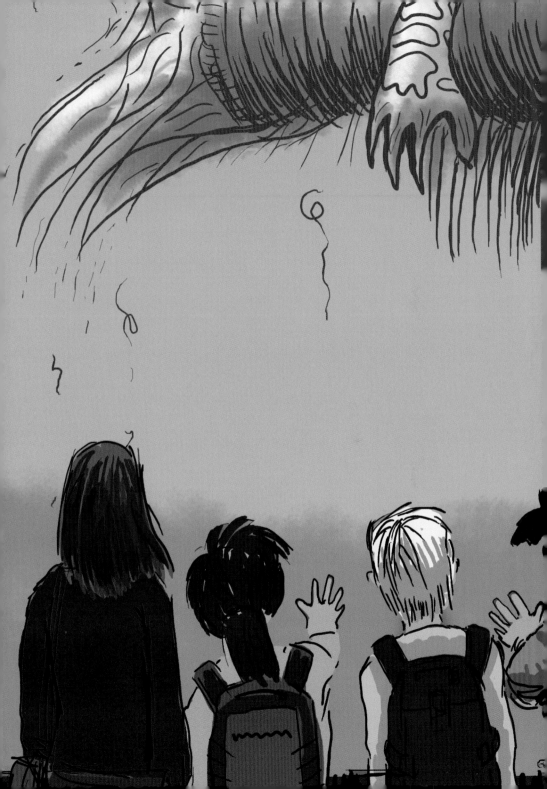

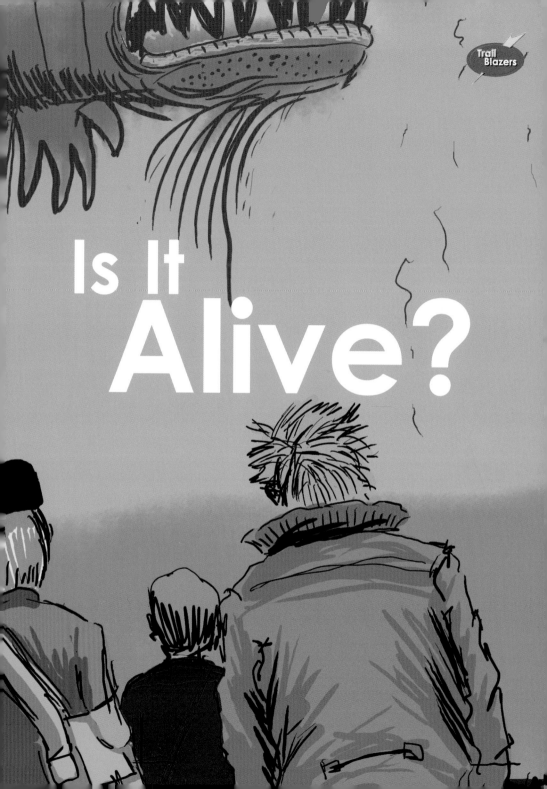

Chapter 1:
A new species

'I've never seen anything like it!'

Beth Childs could hardly believe what she saw in the net. It was a fish, sure, but it was weird.

Its head was huge, and it had eyes that she'd never seen in a fish before. It almost seemed that the fish was watching her. But that was impossible!

'Quick!' shouted Tom. 'Get a tank ready! We've got to get this back to the sea-life centre alive!'

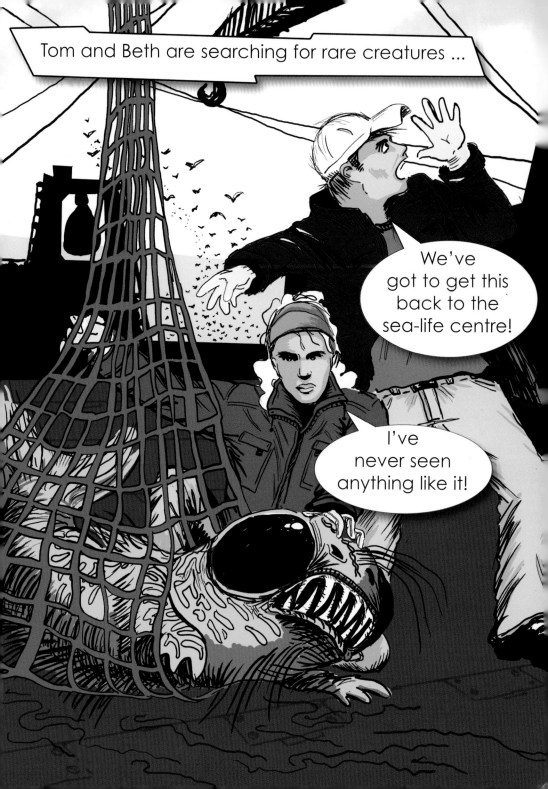

Beth and Tom worked for a sea-life centre in a big city. Visitors came to see the sea creatures in huge tanks. They were on an expedition to find new creatures.

Back at the sea-life centre, Tom checked the description of the fish on the Internet.

'It's a new species!' Tom said. 'Fantastic!'

'There are a lot of sea caves there,' Beth said. 'I think it must have come from one of those.'

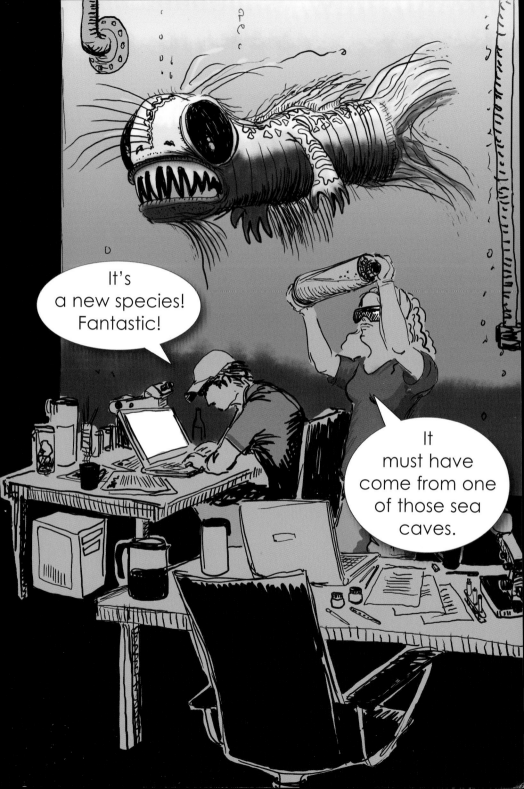

Chapter 2:
Bigeye

The new fish was a great hit at the sea-life centre. It had been given a scientific name, but everyone called it 'Bigeye'.

It spent all its time with its huge head pressed up against the glass. Its eyes stared out at the visitors. Not everyone liked it.

'Those eyes just spook me out!' said one visitor. 'It's horrible!'

Then disaster struck. Bigeye died.

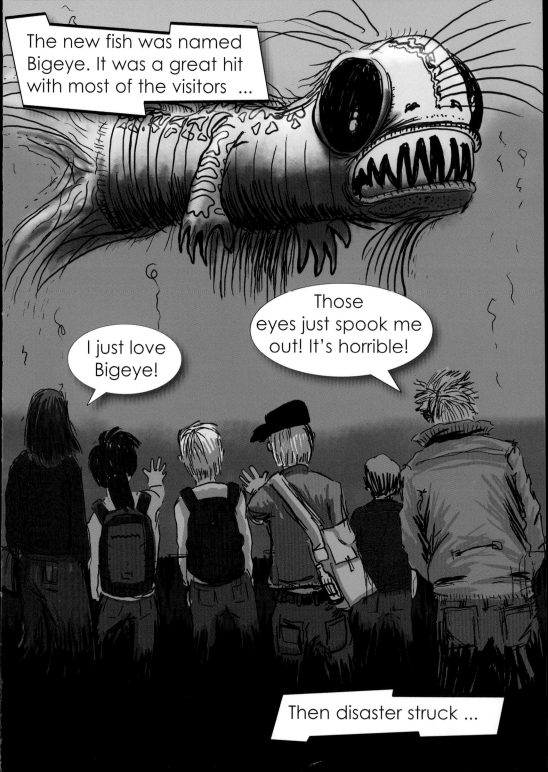

It was Tom's job to check the tanks every morning. He found Bigeye's body floating on the top. Its eyes were cloudy and dull.

The director of the sea-life centre was angry. Business has been great since Bigeye had arrived, but now the fish was dead no one would want to come.

'Are you sure you fed it properly?'

'Quite sure! It loved the meat we gave it. Look how much it's grown!'

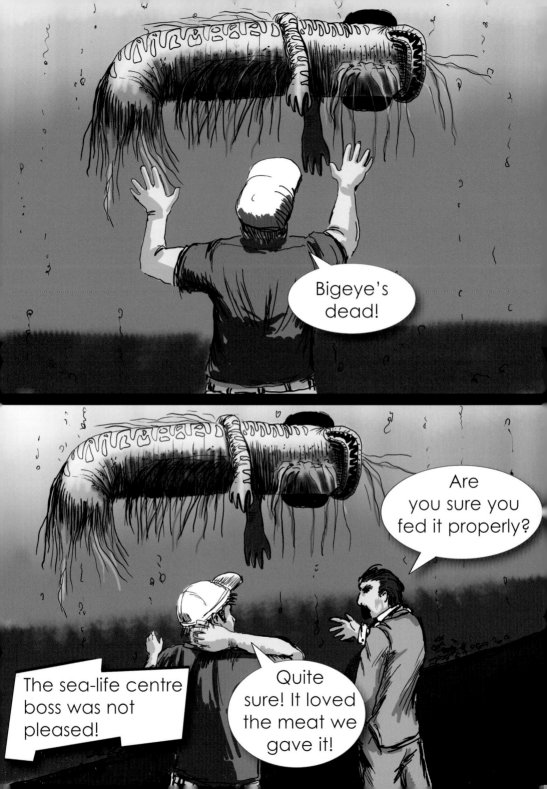

Chapter 3:
It's alive!

In the laboratory of the sea-life centre, Beth got ready to cut up Bigeye. She picked up a sharp knife and held the fish firmly down with her hand.

She had just made the first cut when she felt Bigeye's body moving under her hand.

She dropped the knife and screamed. She couldn't help it.

'It's alive!'

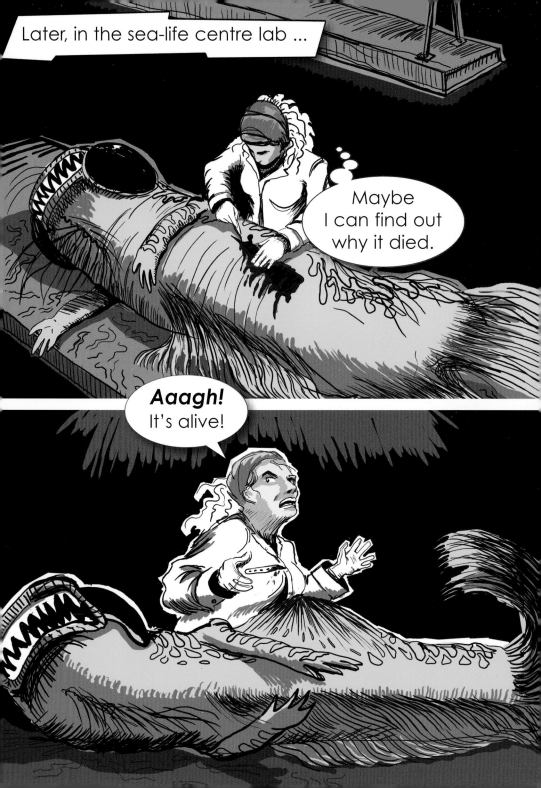

Tom rushed in when he heard the scream.

'What's up?'

'Bigeye's alive!'

'That's impossible!'

'Look!'

Something strange was happening to Bigeye. Its skin was splitting open. Inside its body something was moving, wriggling. Something horrible, like a spider, but with a big head and eyes.

Just like Bigeye.

As they watched, the creature started to eat the body of Bigeye. And it started to grow.

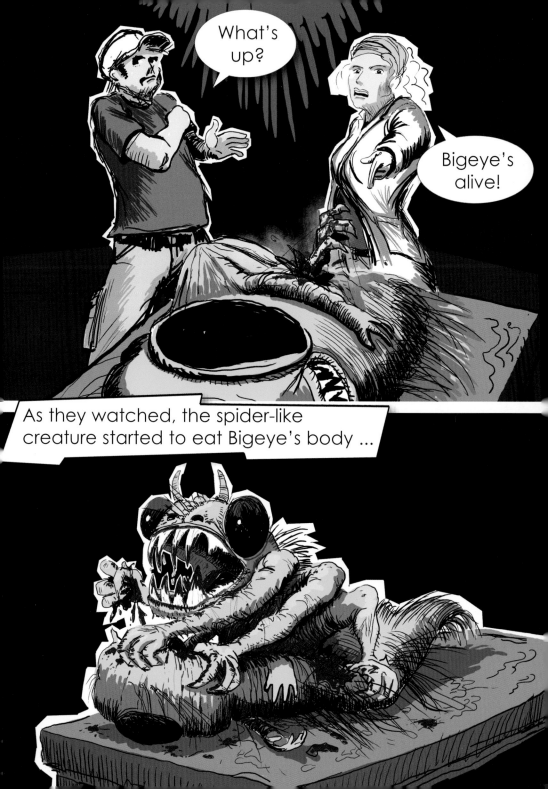

Chapter 4:
A new world

The creature had finished eating Bigeye. It was much bigger now. It jumped down from the table. Tom had left the door open. The creature scuttled through.

'Don't let it get away!'

But the sea-life centre was dark. It was just like the undersea cave that Bigeye had lived in. Except that when it was in its spider form, Bigeye breathed air.

It found a dark corner to hide, where Tom and Beth couldn't find it.

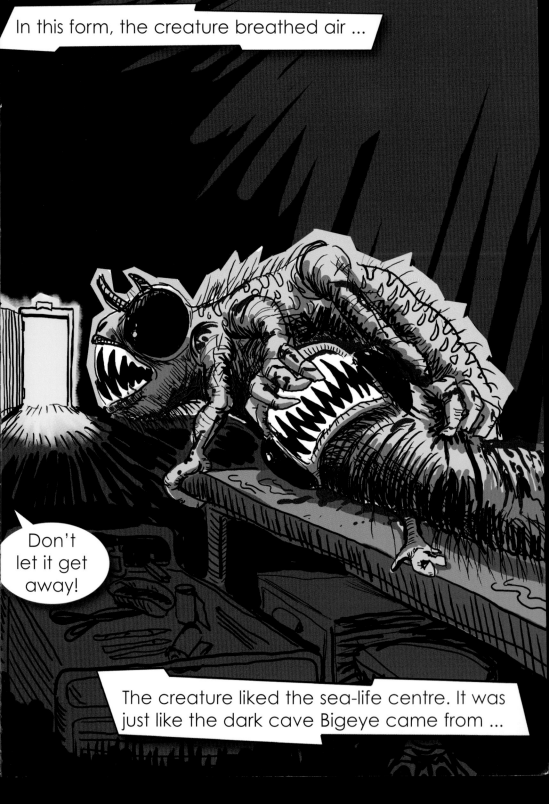

One morning Tom noticed that the tanks had tiny, jelly-like blobs in them – fish eggs!

The eggs started hatching. Out of each one popped a tiny fish, with a big head and huge eyes.

The tiny fishes peered out of the tanks. This was a new world, much better than their cave under the sea!

They would have to get rid of these other creatures if they were going to take it over.

They had ways of doing that.

One morning, Tom was cleaning the tanks ...
There are fish eggs every-where! I wonder where they came from?

The eggs hatched ...
This is a great world to take over! But we'll have to get rid of those other creatures first ...

Weird Creatures word check

adapted	hibernate
Antarctica	predator
black smoker	pressure
camouflage	radiation
chemicals	survive
dehydration	temperature
energy	troglobite
environment	urinate
extremophile	vacuum

The creatures on pages 6 and 7 are:
1. Tarsier
2. Giant prickly stick insect
3. Leafy sea dragon
4. Frogfish
5. Aye-aye
6. Little Dumbo octopus
7. Humpback anglerfish
8. White-faced saki
9. Leaf insect